C000058326

MADAME BILDUNGSROMAN'S
OPTIMISTIC WORLDVIEW

Nora Chassler was born in Madison, Wisconsin, in 1972, and grew up in New York City. She has an undergraduate degree in English from Hunter College, CUNY, in New York, and a Masters in Creative Writing from St Andrews. She has worked as a model and in social work. She lives in Edinburgh.

Her first novel, *Miss Thing*, was published by Two Ravens Press in 2010. Her second, *Grandmother Divided by Monkey Equals Outer Space*, was published by Valley Press in 2015.

Madame Bildungsroman's Optimistic Worldview

NORA CHASSLER

Valley Press

First published in 2017 by Valley Press
Woodend, The Crescent, Scarborough, YO11 2PW
www.valleypressuk.com

First edition, first printing (June 2017)

ISBN 978-1-908853-82-0
Cat. no. VP0099

A CIP record for this book is available from the British Library.

Cover and text design by Jamie McGarry.

Printed and bound in the EU by Pulsio, Paris.

for Airea Dee Matthews

Magic Cast

No sooner had Madame Bildungsroman uttered the sentence 'I refuse to speak in the first person' than things started appearing on her papier-mâché full-body cast, initially on the left forearm. The first words were: cough syrup, tape measure, refills.

A Tree Falls in the Park

A big old tree cracked in half in this morning's gales. Dark, striated and lumpy outside, its inside was peach-coloured. On my way to town I watched fire engines arrive and wee men jump out in yellow vests. They walked slowly around the three-storey fallen tree, scratching their chins.

My mother always said, 'You never know, a flower pot could fly off a sill and brain you'. In high winds I feel like a feather. I huddle in doorways and race to the next shelter. I'm scared I'll be lifted and carried off.

Walking past the wreck on my way home the wind had died down. The fire engines were still there, silent and still, lights flashing like Christmas trees. I didn't see any of the wee men.

Madame Subplot

The proudest moment of my life was when someone read out something I had written that she thought had been written by someone else – but was happy to take the credit for. You can see why normal narratives evade me.

The Castle Door

Oh, K.

Your persistence, alternately whimpering and banging, makes them sick and it makes them laugh. Your selflessness is deeply offensive. Stop your watch. You sleep crouched there! Misdiagnosed intussusception of the ego *will* result; even your mother and sisters will think you failed.

Give up. Just walk away.

No, not *that* way! Walk towards the old Roman bridge. Raise your arms, above your head.

The One Thousand and First Face

It's handy for the storyteller to use characters as metaphors for change. After all, that's what the story assuages – our fear of change. A proper story makes us forget that we have no control of the things we most want to control, and helps us dream of being (or being saved by) heroes. In the story, the hero changes. The truth is people don't; they reveal themselves over time. What's the difference? If you don't know yet you will.

Memory Palaces are the Devil's Work

How can St Augustine hate women with such ugliness and love God with such purity? Why is the brilliant Sherlock Holmes racist? The highest have to choose a lowest. A belief in one's superiority must degrade another. Same principle as profit, and not unrelated. What one has more of has to come out of someone else's pocket, off their plate, out of their body or soul.

People Change Times Don't

A girl in my junior high school wrote that as her yearbook quote by mistake. I didn't mean to say people can't change. I know how upset that makes everyone. I do think the hero is an outmoded paradigm. I'll stand by that.

Mountain

Why is it so important for you to believe that the mountain wouldn't value my tiny admiration and fleeting nature?

Asceticism is for Losers

I'll never forget how bad it made me feel the first time I hit a home run. First pride, then horror. Who had I become?

from *The Table Talk of Madame B.*

'I *believe* in the illusion of free will,' her arm wrote, the words appearing slowly, one letter drawn at a time, from inside the cast.

A Lady I Used to See in Dundee

She had thin, crimped orange hair and was about five years older than me. Her man wore a navy boiler suit. In the mornings, they came out of their ground floor garden flat at the foot of those steps the council had fenced off. They stood just inside the gate, surrounded by garden statues from Poundstretcher and half-full peanut birdfeeders. They grew bright, short flowers. But like the sheer black stockings that she wore with everything – her nurse's shoes, her denim skirts – the garden always seemed doomed and propped up and fake-alive. And the man, he looked like soon enough he'd show his true colours.

Write Livelihood

Livelihood. Such a happy-sounding word. Let me begin by reminding you that not long ago, the noble class to which we all aspired – about whose lives we read, and from whence our fantasies sprang – did not have jobs. And when they did, it was a symptom of their wretchedness. Today we trumpet – we stand proudly behind and uphold with religious fervour – the precept that we all must earn the means to survive through paid labour: we see it as an incontestable moral duty of the highest order.

Can't we find a middle ground and consider the possibility that *some* hard work, some valuable pursuits, might not be compatible with remuneration?

… Thought not.

Price

Why the assumption that what you're willing to do to get something is a good measure of how much you want it?

When Your Mother Sends Back All
Your Invitations

Yesterday I almost mentioned how the workie's hammer (the one that hammered in the garden far away) attached itself to my arm and thence my brain. Turns out it's true what they are saying: the thought starts before you think it.

I also almost told you how the homeopathic finger puppet had supernatural powers, at the same time I internally thanked Steve Aylett.

Finally – weak, very weak, my Chinese acupuncturist said, in Brighton. You can tell him: my pulse isn't weak, it's subtle.

Oh, I forgot, did you notice anyone in the house last night? The utensil wind chime in the pantry went. The fireworks out the window were invisible. And when I looked down on the floor beside my bed, the horns of the beast on the cover of *Myths and Legends of the British Isles* glowed like the eyes of the Hound of the Baskervilles.

Penelope

This morning I lay in bed imagining I was a tree in the middle of an ancient forest. Sometimes people passed; to me, they were like clouds. I felt good when they appreciated my great shape. My pointy hand-leaves. My hundreds of long, long arms. There are years when no consciousness needs me. The other trees, the moss and tall grass speak only of their wounds. The forest animals are task-obsessed. 'Winter this' and 'summer that'. The air is saying the same thing over and over without pause, and it's the opposite of boring.

What Did Louis Althusser and Norman Mailer Have in Common?

No – not the wife thing. It has to do with their relationship to lies. Does a good storyteller know they are lying? Does it matter if a great interpreter has read the primary text?

The Angel in the Hoose

All the men I've ever loved have made a point early on of telling me they were shallow. Like I fucking care.

The Enlightenment

About a hundred years ago there was a witch who lived in Edinburgh, on the top floor of a tenement. She'd lived in the same flat since she was a wee girl, when it was new-built.

There was a small pantry with a door behind the kitchen. Her father and her brother and her husband were not allowed in. Her mother had died and the witch had two sons. Her husband and brother and father had done very well in their business; they owned three tailor-shops. They could have afforded to move to a flat on the first floor but they believed the top flat had brought them luck: a house full of boys and wealth. The fact that the witch's mum had died young didn't seem like bad luck. It was God gaining an angel.

Anyway, in her cupboard the witch ... did nothing really. She didn't light candles; she recited no spells. She squatted on the floor and closed her eyes and was able to remember life in the womb. When I say *remember*, I mean she could feel how she felt: suspended and warm, always ready for a reverse movement, intentionless. Whether this practice – which she undertook for about an hour a day – brought her family their good luck is anyone's guess. I'm just telling you what she told me when I met her this morning in the pantry. As she spoke, the drier ran behind her.

I asked her what her name was and it was hard to hear her over the din when she replied, 'The thought at the end.'

Jim'll Fix It *or* Cold-Blooded Common Sense

Wanting things you can't have makes life hell. Either figure out how to get them, or how not to want them.

Gratitude

Successful people can be very superstitious. They worship causation: their understanding of it is poor. (Their insight having paused at the many-armed demi-god of personal charms, prejudices, protocols, narratives, verboten foods, family ties, haunted trees etc.)

No one understands the real value of luck like the luckless. The lack of which can grant great freedom: superstition's power has been disproven so many times that they no longer spare it a thought – therein lies a shortcut to a lower tier of enlightenment.

Kind of like one of those bonus holes in a pinball machine, the one that gives you an extra ball.

Haar

The children woke early and then I did. They pointed out a new mountain, mostly hidden behind the one that's always there. It was similar in shape but half as tall and wide again. The mist was heavy on it. We told the others. They rubbed their eyes. For us, mountains appear and disappear every day. All things are changing; some have patterns, others surprise you.

A month ago a woman said that *everything* here has patterns, just that some we couldn't see or didn't understand.

She was sent away.

Homunculi

There are miniature workmen in wee yellow jackets inside Madame B's papier-mâché shell. It's the only possible explanation. Who else could be in the act of writing?

Smoke and Mirrors

You asked me why I didn't ask her how she got the job. I reminded you I had and she'd said: *it's all smoke and mirrors.*

You, who have gone so far in the world, looked surprised. I don't know why, it's your MO too. You're convinced your success is the product of a painstaking fraud. You refuse to reveal even the rules you think you're breaking! Superstition? A bizarre form of modesty?

Translation from that language in my brain I don't speak

Why is it worse, youth buried in an old face than age in a young one? It's the unknown again, our total dependence on *what comes next*. But the truth, which is not said and not known, rattles on, behind the action. We cover the grave so well. Our destination's the biggest bluff of all.

Weakness

What does fighting do to you? Why do you think it's weakness that keeps me from fighting? I don't like to feel hate.

Surprise Ending My Ass

All the beginnings and middles and ends we import from stories and graft onto our lives. Why do we dwell on the moments that take us away from what's plain as day – there is no narrative like that here. But art will go on cooking it up and we will swallow it whole.

When I was a girl they said they told stories so that I could never forget all the bad things we are capable of, and so that I would understand the importance of love.

Take Me to Your Leader

The way you see it, you can experience the heady emotion of the moment, or not. Then you die. Exploring what you might learn about yourself by observing these emotions – because for you thought is not only *not* emotional, but *cancels out emotions* – is a total downer and waste of time. You're utterly convinced; whatever you're unfortunate enough to learn by accident will never come up again.

How Much for Your World View

City Daughter.

One of those bad days when all half-open shutters show vases of dusty fake flowers, and green striped wallpaper, and corners of polished end tables that seem no less important than glimpses of the unknown universe, dark matter... These rooms I see from the crappy, rainy streets urge an awful, deep, relentless need to be someone else. Different loves, jobs, children.

What is your life, what's in your room, what do you know for sure?

If Sleep Was the Invention of a Science Fiction Author We'd All Think it Was Absolutely Fucking Brilliant

For a few days I thought about a little gun that had appeared in an unfinished story I wrote twenty years ago.

This morning I kept seeing a little knife, a mini machete, and with its hook I imagined tracing the rhombus I'd cut to remove my heart.

My brother had a dream when he was young that a robin flew into his chest and that his ribs opened like a book and inside was a classroom with people with oranges for heads standing in front of a blackboard. Or maybe I am misremembering that.

In this kitchen everything is made out of squares.

At the gene clinic the lady took a long family history, and made a family tree where the women were circles and the men were squares. If they had cancer they got a messy black dot in them.

Why are light fixtures round and cupboards square? I love convention. I live for convention.

The Bell was Also Tolling

I wish to God I could remember if it was the seagull eating the crow or the crow eating the seagull. That sums me up. Why the hell can't I remember the detail humans value most: who did what to whom.

These two were at the top of a wide, dark, curvy and steep flight of church steps in Dundee. It was pishin' doon. A few people passed.

The guts were open like a book, the size of both my palms. The wound was red as only wet red can be. Ruby slippers. The scavenger was struggling with some very long, stringy bits.

Bronx Science

I felt so alone at my desk and the ceiling light was too bright. The articles I'd read and ripped from *Scientific American* went in one file folder in the stiff drawer. I'd watched too much TV, and fun and love was all very far from blood types, cow ventricles, graphs demanding immense patience and *damaged* by empathy. I moved out into the day, drunk, because I was bored senseless the instant I arrived. And I remain there. My boredom has taken on fantastical hues. I hallucinate.

Pin-Headed Angels Dreaming

We never liked the "strange loop" thing. It seemed another turn of the human-bound kaleidoscope, another attempt to *prove it wasn't* but this time by saying *it was*. That's just where we are at at the moment, art is doing it too.

Still, rational thought predates what we now see fit to apply it to. Alchemy was pretty logical, it just didn't work. We created everything we created via *how we thought it through*. First we knew the process. Then we cast about for what it would work on. We knew how it had to work in order for it to work. Your mobile's not a miracle.

FRAGILE

When we were young there were more boxes and crates with FRAGILE stickers on them; giant video cameras packed tight in grey foam, synthesisers in wooden trunks. You could sit on them on the corner or the subway platform. Am I alone in not wanting everything shrunk as small as possible? Where is everything?

Teeth

I was looking at my daughter's teeth in the dentist's chair. The dentist said they were great. My attachment to my daughter and to her teeth was so strong. I love her teeth. I thought about a parent on that flight that got shot down in the Ukraine, loving their child's perfect teeth. And then of course all the gory details of the news story... identifying remains.

I mention this because I try not to name that kind of over-powering, visceral attachment, though now that I write it I think that's pretty silly of me, because I feel it *all the time*, so who cares if I name it or not? Maybe dwelling with it in its unnamed state seems safer; it's like a dream. I read somewhere recently that dreams were like stories. Not mine. My dreams are about places. The action is a marble in one of those vertical mazes, or water filling up a tub. How to deal with the place. That's my job in my dreams.

They made me think about vegetarianism, the teeth. And about how attached most animals are to their lives, and the lives of their loved ones. Humans who purport to be far along the spiritual path extol non-attachment as the highest spiritual achievement, while at the same time urging us to respect another's attachment to being alive.

Depth of Field

Your iPhone can filter your holiday snap into a fake Ansel Adams. But what an old camera can do – because it *adds itself* instead of *subtracting you* – is entirely different. It's the medium – *its* qualities, *its* limitations, and the artist's and the viewer's interaction with them – that makes great art.

I think the same might go for the infuriating, static page of yore. It forces you alive. It adds the reader and helps the writer.

Which Is As it Should Be?

You work as hard as you can to make perfect objects, with an order inside that's mostly unseen, with a coherence that makes you the opposite of dizzy. When you meet the breakfast mess it breaks your heart: the things you needed to impress on the world couldn't be more absent. Your thought and your conjuring doesn't mean shit. Real life depresses you, even when it's not being sad. From now on you refuse to take art seriously – let it do that itself. You're applying for that import/export position after all. You'll see if things will reverse: will you work hard in real life, discover meaning there, and cry at the sight of art?

El Bosque

There's never a 'Why', we figured that out, and switched to cause: sunlight made this DNA mutate; oxytocin caused that warmth. O, our grasp of cause has made us capable of such effects!

'Why' is God now God is dead. I, for one, pursue it endlessly, with a childish heart full of faith. People look away when I talk; it is an embarrassment. For ten thousand hours of attention I'm very lucky to poke one pinhole of light through this shitty sheet of black construction paper we call consciousness. And even that prick is probably a hallucination.

Why does God insist on being? We kill and kill and kill but meaning sprouts anew.

Consciousness is a coppiced wood and trees are words.

Learning to Read

Maybe it's true what you said, and I read wrong.

I couldn't read until I was nine but when I could, perhaps due to the massive build up, I believed. I brought everything to it. Now, most things I write mean at least two other things. This supersaturation is something I suspect it would be as hard for me to shake as for some people to produce. We all have our foibles.

I was writing about the places in narrative where authority gains our loyalty. The thrill of the story is all well and good, but you have to question what the story upholds, structurally.

I'm sorry, but a narrative is often not the liberating journey the press-release would have you believe. It's the vehicle for various propagandas: of identity, class, gender, whatever needs cementing at a given time and place. And women are trained to be vulnerable to the frisson of apology. I don't make this stuff up.

The Sappy Bit

My daughter's revulsion at the end of films when the man apologises (usually it's a man; I'd argue the motif is based on that of a man apologising, even when a woman has replaced him) makes me proud. I think her sickening at sap is healthy. And here's a riddle: what are the other times when, after inflicting some harm on us, the boss comes home, says sorry and wants a hug? It becomes about him. It becomes about the fact that he loves you, when actually the whole narrative was about what he put you through. Forgiveness is the key to those scenes my daughter hates. But that's not real forgiveness; it's *forgetness*. It's: 'Forget why this all happened and focus on me. Forget I caused the problem and believe I'm the only one who can fix it. You can't get better without me.' Which is utter bullshit.

Self-Control

It doesn't get any more unfashionable than good old-fashioned self-restraint. Capitalism needs it like a hole in the head, as much as the Church needed equality. But self-control is how we grow spiritually. Cut back a dog rose; fix it to a stone wall; it makes a lovely shape; it's healthier and so is the whole garden. We have to do that to ourselves. (Obviously, there are occasions when you need to detach from the wall, get blown about and risk death in the storm. But as a general rule: stay within limits.)

NYC

I wonder if it's still fashionable for beers to wear paper bags there.

The White Dot Waving

The white dot is every woman in your story because the white dot is the blind spot, her self, and you're a mirror.

X

Women go to such great lengths to deny that they fall out of love, that they will, and that they have.

Before the Married Women's Property Act of 1870

It's interesting to note that romance reached its peak in the Brontes' gothic novels, where the ultimate act of chivalry involves the hero pissing-the-fuck-off, dropping dead or – at the very least – being badly maimed.

One Summer

I went to Moscow in 1992. We rode on a sleeper train from Prague. A fat engineering student who shared our cabin also shared the jam his mother made with us; he put it in our tea. In the middle of the night we pulled into a barn where they lifted the train high above the tracks, and put it back down again. On the walls, there were peace posters with doves and olive branches – in Russian, obviously. Three old ladies told me I was pretty – inside and out – when, in the morning, as I smoked out the train window, I stood aside to let them pass in the narrow coach hall. I had a shaved head at that time. In Moscow, we stayed in a communal apartment. I drank too much vodka and was terrified to leave our room, a beautiful old ballroom with dozens of mosquitos on the white walls. In the kitchen, one of the tenants, a pretty anchorwoman, had left a raw joint of beef out. I couldn't believe an anchorwoman lived in a communal apartment. She left it for two days.

Abstraction

Your thoughts aren't in your head.

CostaStarbucksNeroeternity

Suddenly, I understand why I avoid them. It's not a snob thing (as you insist). This is the fiction version of the real living room of most people's childhoods: men sitting alone soothed, aroused and angry (to varying degrees) among groups of women, gossiping, with babies, chatting, ordering cakes and bathtubs of hot milk.

The women's chatter is so unimportant, in such clean and certain tones – it's somehow immoral.

And everyone – except that very skinny Chinese guy who ordered a double espresso to go, put three straws of sugar in it and ran away – seems very comfortable. *Too* comfortable!

Ok… maybe it is a snob thing, or worse, misanthropy.

Just tell me one thing: *why does it take so fucking long and cost so fucking much?*

And while I'm here waiting, you know: the exponential rise in prescriptions of anti-anxiety SSRIs coincides nicely with these sinkfuls of coffee they sneak in with your milk. Happy coincidence? *I doubt it!*

Ok, I have my giant cappuccino now. I'll be on my merry way.

Self-Consciousness

For the Romantics, it was a vital element of art; for their descendants, a failing, a weakness. Why? And please don't say 'it meant something else then'. Because I'm not talking about self-consciousness along the lines of 'I have a zit and I feel self-conscious about it'. I refuse to accept that that lovely, complex thought – the one that follows almost every thought worth thinking – has lost its meaning for us. Oh, sorry … what *is* that thought? It's the one that asks: why did I think that?

Ignorance

Not wanting to know and not caring are often opposites.

Birthday

When I was a little girl, old ladies wore hats, often with nets that covered their faces, and they always wore gloves, and never, ever wore sneakers. They were small, like I was.

Maybe the lack of HRT.

My Birthday Wish

Once you die you're in every universe at once.

Mental Maths

I couldn't count on my fingers because I thought it was the space you should count and not the finger. Also the first one can't be one yet. One comes after something. I think it says that in the Old Testament.

Blockages

I have a friend who told me she removed her own hymen so her boyfriend 'wouldn't have the satisfaction'. At the time I thought it was cool but now it seems sad.

Recently she told me she was throwing out all her writing. She used to write, but 'kept the diary of ten million teenage girls in her heart'. She said the journals and pages now hampered her, and she wanted to get rid of them before 'someone else had to feel guilty for throwing it all away once she was dead'. That just seemed weird. She was 40. I think she had saved all those pages in the hope that someone would want to read them eventually; and when she realised they probably wouldn't, she got rid of them.

She seemed ok about it. She looks ok. I think she's fine. Anyway what could *I* do? Offer to read it? Are you crazy?

Half of Life is Getting There

My abiding belief that this life is a tiny part of an endless whole we know nothing about isn't the worry. I can prove that. What really ends but things that humans create? Endings are imaginary. Nor does anything start when you think it does. And regarding whether I will know or not, I don't care at all.

Bitter thought

The thing famous people fail to grasp is that people are nicer to them.

You Weren't *Really* Shocked Now, Were You?

Real shock is rare. What we mistake it for is usually just a blunder. Take ten steps back: you can see most events that concern you coming. My personal style is to discount things as impossible when they are simply too stupid. Yours will be different. Whatever flavour your self-deception, look to the story. Compare what was there to what you made of it. See the dots – now take a look at how you connected them. Now erase those wee lines. The dots are still there; they tell you all there is to know. There is no plot here.

The End of the School Run

My daughter pointed out that the route we take across the park has changed slightly. She said: you overshot again. Arthur's Seat was now in the middle of my course and it used to be on the right. I said, I suspect it's some atavistic thing; I'm following a shift in the sun's trajectory. She said, that makes a lot of sense, given our purposes. Unaccountably flustered, I defended myself: well, it was probably a very useful way of making assignations in the distant past! Then I pivoted into line, and was relieved when the subject changed to that pug we pass who pees and shits at the same time.

A little further on, as we walked through the growing real estate development, I told her that the last patch of sky would soon be gone from that section of our walk. The final building is going up, filling the missing tooth of the street. She asked, where does air go when we build and build? I told her I didn't know; I suspected air couldn't go anywhere. I thought, in windows? nowhere? up? She said, I like caverns anyway.

Xanax, or Man, Would You Have Loved These!

You take one at 10pm because you are scared and want to sleep. A warm blur of plans free of doubt – then, the heavenly drop of a feather; you don't wake once in the night (usually it's about thirty times). Hey, it's tomorrow! 10am and your eyes blink open like a doll's. Throughout the day, a nagging loss; where are your dreams?

Lou Reed's Liver

How bad could he have been if Laurie Anderson loved him?

Stories vs. People

They say that narratives are a balm for the chaos of lived experience. Just desserts, comeuppance, lessons learned, etc. But if the story suppresses and contradicts the experience of being here, is it worth it? If the story makes you long for a world where there is an author – or worse, makes you believe there actually may be – then the structure is doing more harm than good.

God

I'm not saying there isn't a God. Just that if there is, she isn't a storyteller.

No One Listens to Reason

That's why God has to pretend to be a zealot.

Lilya Brik

You may know her from that Rodchenko poster; she's half-woman, half-megaphone. What a gorgeous profile! She's got a scarf on her head. Her mouth is wide open like a cave in a cliff; words are marching out looking healthy and brave. She had quite a life! Which brings me to Mme B, who does not. Who, this morning at breakfast, spoke for the first time in weeks. There was a lot of throat clearing. She smokes. She said, 'We would like to request to be Lilya Brik now.'

Person

According to Chambers dictionary: a living soul.

My Little Comeback

If narrative immersion's all you want there's no reason to bother with the written word. Just watch something, like *Game of Thrones* or *My Little Pony*.

Free To Be You and Me

It turned out that, thanks to influences subtle and deep – not directed, that's important – my friend embodied … certain ideals; let's leave it at that.

I am pretty sure that any human quality that feels authentic, truly beautiful even, is born this way: it mustn't be intentional.

My point? Authenticity is – sine qua non – the only thing that *reads*.

(That said, there are bigger and smaller, friendlier and crueler, smarter and dumber truths; the hard thing to stomach is that yours may be too odd, after all that feeling, what a shame … I'd still say persist, though I can't tell you why.)

My Lovely Lady Humps

For much of human history the most important words we heard made no sense to us; we literally couldn't understand what the priest said. Even when it was in our native tongue we couldn't understand the symbolism, the strange stories with no end, the lists. We spent our lives decoding. We trusted when we couldn't understand. And we felt soothed in not knowing. It was the sound, and the speaker, and what we were told they meant. It was where they stood. And what they wore. But it was also this value of words. We know and we don't know, at best.

Was there a point in time, along the lines of when perspective was invented, when words were relieved of these, their highest uses?

Literature was not always so far from the other arts, from music and visual images. Today we are allowed to stand in front of a painting and not get it, but still love it. Likewise, music.

Is the highest words can climb the pop song lyric, the poem that tells you something about love or death or longing – reminds you of something you've felt? (I won't even mention that one story we are allowed to tell.) What about following a thought, or a set of images, or events, a long list even, and trying to understand what it means? This in itself is a lost art.

I don't always have to say something you understand.

Channeling Frank Zappa *or* Guru School Drop-out

Never give me any money. I'm a chancer.

Frankly My Dear

The idea that we could imagine with any accuracy the mindset of a human in a previous time has been pretty convincingly challenged by New Historicism, IMHO. But I guess a historical novelist can always cite *Gone With the Wind* as evidence to the contrary.

Burns Night

The Scottish Passover. Same wan pride at being on the long time losing side. Same endless meal and drunken speechifying. Same spotty observance from year to year. But most of all – the same absolute horror at one's national cuisine.

Genius

Genius can't happen without the artist's belief in the separation of themselves from their art. The usual manifestation is via BPD (Bad Personality Disorder). In those instances, their chaotic ugliness plays foil to the perfection of their creation. But there's nothing inherent that says they *need* that juxtaposition – it's simply ready to hand, as their art has gained them power. They might instead *just not identify themselves with their art*. But that would take *work*, and they are very busy.

Guilt

Everyone wants to believe they are innocent, some more than others – and they are easy to find. Next, accuse them of being guilty and low. Now, watch them suffer. (Added bonus: they won't flee. They'll stay right where they are, trying to prove themselves to you.)

Who would do such a thing? Ministers, for one.

Cynicism

Often telling the truth, freed from sentiment, is considered cynical. Why? An appraisal of the facts doesn't erase feelings, it just omits them from analysis. The problem is that we mix sentiment with fact; we confuse and conflate them. Of course they co-exist. But very often, both inter-personally and as a widespread social tool, feelings are exploited, and used to make us do things that are not in our best interests.

My point: feel all you want, I know I fucking do. I just caution you not to follow your feelings unthinkingly. Observe them first. Who's under there? Who said that? Why? Etc. Now decide what to do. I guess that's cynical? Weird.

Evil

You said stories were invented to blood-let fear, to contain and control it, and the unknown in general. You said sometimes folk took advantage and used narratives to coerce and brainwash. That wasn't what I meant. I simply said stories were invented as a technology of control and that evil is fictive.

Leaves

Shush. Listen to the motiveless leaves. Now that it's cold they are coated in frost. They are cracking under your footsteps! It's the beginning of your day and the end of theirs. Luckily, they don't care. They have been through a lot: sheer experience without struggle requires all their energy. And is nothing like as easy as it looks.

The Geographic

Places have feelings too. Dundee would have done anything for me. It gave my daughter a brand new school. It gave me the snowstorm and light of a lifetime and a lovely house... New York always held it against me. Why didn't I do what any sane person would do, and sell what I had been given? If I didn't (and I wouldn't) it had me understand that I could get the fuck out. And Edinburgh? Edinburgh is as neutral as a feeling thing can be. Thoughts come through my feet as I walk over the mounds of the Meadows. The city neither flatters me nor despairs at my failures. It seems to take me as I am. Half-dead among its sleepy living and lively ghosts.

Meet Me Anywhere but at the Book Fair

When writers are in the presence of their fans they can't see straight. A newly-adored writer is a fun house mirror for readers' projections; a writer for whom it's old hat is a corpse strapped into a roller coaster.

Prozac

Lightens your spirit and puts your soul to sleep.

Meaning and the Narrative Mind

A dead sparrow at the school gates, and the fear of its meaning gripping me. Portents. Omens. Garbage, and the equivalent of misconstruing déjà vu. The future is indeed here now – but its arrival in the form of a symbol is as silly as the idea that man is formed in the image of God.

Novel Descending a Staircase

In its prime, in its Usefulness, the novel was 'the individual versus society' – by which we meant: read how the mechanism of his culture destroys this fine man's soul. Slowly the novel has changed. Now: look into his nasty interior. How much like yours it is!

Poor Tess

Sometimes it's good to remind yourself that 'fallen woman' is an official Library of Congress film genre.

The Start of Chapter Five

The young woman reading her text message. Standing frozen in a circle of very pretty dead leaves. Her face composed and ecstatic. Only one thing looks like that.

More Problems for the Poor Artist

When you aren't given what's owed you as a human – and almost no one on earth is – you tend to glorify what life would be like if you had it. Unfortunately, this may have a deleterious effect on your art: it may be sentimental, and rife with simplistic fantasies of redemption.

The solution, the skeleton key for the have-not, is the double remove: even your own folk must reject you. Or you can reject them – either works.

The second you grasp that nothing will repair your deepest problems, your production values go through the roof, or glass ceiling.

(And btw the only fraternity at the top involves agreement on who to keep down; those guys feel less akin to each other than they do to us. Maybe this is why their art tends to be infuriatingly good. They know there's no redemption here. They have had everything that their hearts desired.)

Looking for the Lyrical

Where's it gone? We used to embed with care, a golden egg in straw, a setting sun. Among high notions. High. Now, where? It's not in the *Guardian* (they're too obsessed with Miley Cyrus). It's not in the pop songs about how women love to be treated badly. Where did it go? I can't see it anywhere. (Looks around frantically.)

It's a bit like that book about film editing, *The Conversations*. He says: cut out what you think is the most important thing in the scene. Great advice. But maybe history and culture at large does that too? History is a great big noisy performance artist, in her own way...

I'm not talking about death and pain. That's the lyric's still-born sister. I'm talking about the sheer and delicate elation at being here – *in spite of* death and pain.

I attempt this carefully, not out of coyness or craftiness, but because the lyric is intrinsically silent; she dies on her own. She needs a house, a story, bubble wrap.

Origin

There once was a frog named Suzanne. Who ate all the bugs in the pond. Her tummy swelled and her pad buckled under. For a time she was swallowed, into the green. She sank like a stone.

But after a month Suzanne bobbed up, a dead frog.

A tow-headed girl came along. She fashioned a stretcher from twigs. The sun was bright over the pond and the dead frog's flesh was like a dirty stained glass window.

Upon Suzanne the girl laid hands – with no luck. So she set about cutting the frog up. She spread her entrails on a folding beach chair and studied them like stars.

The tow-headed girl is a prize-winning scientist today. She continues to dream, unconsciously, of healing with magic.

My Wee PTSD

What is the solution to trauma? Repress it and it just pops up somewhere else wearing a creepy mask. See it as it is. Stare it straight in the face. Go everywhere with it. Treat it like your kid. Buy it sweeties. Talk to it about things other than itself. Distract it with 'the wonders of the natural world'. Above all, don't let it be scary. It's just a bit fucked up, like the rest of us.

Top

I remember being less than two and labouring with a metal spinning top; you had to balance it on its point first, and then pump with a stiff red handle. We were visiting someone, and there was nothing else to do; at least this was clearly the appropriate and quiet choice. My brother was elsewhere and wouldn't have wanted to hang out with me. The adults only appreciated conversation and I didn't have anything to say.

As I played with the toy I thought about something someone must have told me. How the earth went around the sun, how the sun was in space, and how big space was. I imagined myself a filament, packed tightly with others on the surface of the earth. We were swinging around our sun. We could see countless other suns, in envelopes of galaxies that – respiring and piled on top of each other – splayed out to the sides and slowly changed places, like animals in a herd. The idea of all this, and of my insignificance in particular, made me happier than anything ever had. My only slight regret (how human) was that I hadn't been born knowing.

Losing

Christmas is such a cheery season, especially for one as upbeat as our hollow heroine, Mme B. An eye is drawn on anywhere, and she's pulled to the kitchen, feeling like a ghost in the red Christmas lights. The papier-mâché effigy reflects – propped up by the table, over an empty mug of pretend coffee – on how she never hopes anymore. She hopes for health for those she loves, and happiness – but not for things of your world, as the sole of her right foot puts it. Her strange inside-writing-men are using crappy pens today: old striating magic markers. Rising from my reading-station like a suitor asking for her dead hand, I return to my chair and drink my real coffee. Look at her: letters appearing and disappearing on her paper body like clouds moving across the sky; string mop signifying *my* hair. I feel so close to her but I wish she said other things.

Sad Truth #57,262

The things publishers look for are not inside books.

Sappho

In answer to that question people ask: if you could go back in time and meet anyone...

Sappho, I choose you.

Obviously, I will want to see the lovely dresses you wore, your red gold hair, and the male and female beauties that you loved so hard (or said you did). I want to see the trees you walked by. And meet your daughter. Maybe you can show me what you wrote? All that stuff that got lost. Mostly though, I'm interested in what you saw. I know you can't not tell me the truth. How was the story-as-we-know-it implanted in our hearts? Where did the Furies go in their earliest exile? Behind a dune? What kept them warm at night? Did they have a fire? What I really want, Sappho, are your eyes – the last pair.

In the Disappearing Process

I guess it's a bit like Photoshopping to produce graininess, or black and white: these were elements of film. They are not integral to digital photography. Why add them in? We need to find each medium's unique strengths. Though we might start by asking if digital cameras, smartphones and software are mediums in the traditional sense.

Technology

Maybe I'm confusing 'medium' with 'technology'.

Etymologies Don't Always Help

'Technology' comes from the word 'skill'. 'Medium' from 'middle'. That really cleared things up…

False Dichotomy

The Wise Woman/Cynic split. My own bespoke Madonna/Whore!

Vision on George IV Bridge

Two girls in matching supernova leggings.

The Guts of a Black Hole

There is new evidence suggesting that what we thought was the mysterious 'dark matter' in black holes is actually nickel and iron. Early findings indicate these elements are in the form of the contents of a kitchen drawer that existed twenty-five years ago, in New Jersey.

Question for those on SSRIs

What's the relation between our tendency to obsessive thought, religious litany and fear of death? A: Who cares!

Feldenkrais

How you get places – whether you drive or walk – completely affects what you see, and the pace and pattern of your thoughts and emotions. Interactions between cars are far more rule-bound and therefore aggressive than those between pedestrians. The ground you cover and how you cover it is not a metaphor.

Low

I know the top chakra is above us. Why isn't there one below us, too? Not 'your grounding', but where you are actually standing, *the ground,* what you walk on. I think you should burn your car.

Also: I know chakras don't exist, but in all fairness, neither do you.

Boozelessness

A problematic state of being, translated from the German. To name one of its many oppressive constituents: this tightly stitched, repetitive coherence. Drunkenness passes, ebbs and flows; we can surprise and appall ourselves in its flabby arms. Sobriety is fucking endless. Staring out to sea with the same set of eyes. Day in, day out. You start to understand why people do things like jump out of airplanes.

Winning Near the Goal

I know a man who has to calculate for everything; that's how he puts it. He thinks he knows what causes what. Actually it's only his calculations that determine the result.

River City

I wake up feeling like a misused dolly grip on the soap opera of you. I was hired as an outsider, with a set of vital, background expertise; and now, somehow, I'm playing the lady of the house, cheated of her inheritance, flaring my nostrils, storming around in a silk kimono. Can I go back to adjusting for smoothness, keeping the imperceptible imperceptible? It's my calling.

While I'm here: I won't be in tomorrow. I have to go to the optometrist. I think I might need glasses; I can barely read the cue cards so I'm making up half my own lines. The sad part is none of you have noticed. Who writes this shit?

Good to Know...

Jonathan Edwards died of a smallpox vaccination. Wittgenstein and Hitler went to the same school at the same time. Charles Manson auditioned for the Monkees.

Nationalism

Why is team building considered a good idea even for a second?

Omniscience

Madame B and I fell out. She said: can't I at least read a Terry Pratchett?

I accused her of all sorts of shirking. She shredded.

She's in pieces and insists on nothing now.

She can read serious literature or nothing at all. And yes, that would be abusive and controlling if she wasn't a figment of my imagination.

I'm returning to my novel – the one written by a rock that developed a face by forming itself over millions of years around fossils that look like eyes, a nose and mouth.

I don't need her scrappy ass!

Westerns

I fucking hate Westerns. A description of a prairie or a caravan of covered wagons, a hard-ass frontier town – makes me want to puke. Must be some repressed childhood memory. Or maybe an unrepressed cultural one.

Why I don't daydream

I'll write a bestseller by Darwina James. It will be called *The Cougar*, and be a garden variety wish-fulfillment fantasy – with bells on! It will raise the tastes of the atavistic saddos who loved *Fifty Shades* and be loosely based on that woman who is directing the movie (the irony won't be lost on her). The writing will have to be toned down; I'll use 'times' for 'zeitgeist' – this kind of thing – but that won't matter. It will be carefully plotted, just the right amount of scenes without promise of sex; it will be neatly linear, with a very happy ending that seals it tight – like a can of tomatoes! And I will be fêted and rich and even have the chance to be a real-life cougar myself.

Now that I am thinking about it I can't see any advantages this plan would incur for me or the reader.

Epic Confusion

Post-movie novels, in a flailing and barely-perceived attempt at self-preservation, have gone up their own arses. Metaphors, handy for the visual description, gorgeous – nay – vital accoutrements at the sentence level, have swollen into themes. The shed represents his hurt heart, the beehive her unfulfilled sexual urges. Gimme a fucking break. Have their house be their house; the hard part is individuation. (Ironically, today the thing publishers most fear.) Novelists: if you feel usurped by movies (one symptom is total dominance of the visual imagination), either stop watching them for a long time and clean out your brain, or write a new kind of story. Ask yourself: what needs saying now. And please don't hide the answer inside a fake book.

Vegetarians

I'm sure it's just my skewed perception, but they seem to dislike live animals too. I've known several who showed a marked coldness towards the cuddliest of pets.

I'm Not a Vegetarian but I Play One on TV

I was going to take myself to a Japanese place for lunch but wanted to be alone. I was starving and had had no breakfast.

I rushed in the door. That tin of French pâté someone brought back… too small for more than one. No preservatives.

It was great.

I think about the life of the animal as I eat it. Not as a punishment, it's a habit I got into. Usually, I buy meat that's had 'a good life'. This one worried me. We know how the French treat farm animals. I was apologising in my head, when I heard a voice shout at me like a horn, in an accent like Ratatouille's:

'I am a French pig! I lived inside all my life to make this wonderful food for you and I am proud! And I'd do it again and again! How dare you malign me, you stupid American person!'

Who knew farm animals could be crazy too? It makes sense I guess.

1980s Jungian Cookbook (for my dad)

A Warburton's toaster muffin with bacon and ketchup tastes *exactly* like the steamed pork buns we used to get in Chinatown.

Translation from the Yiddish

There was a mayfly that married a pebble. The mayfly loved honey and jam.

The pebble loved nothing.

The mayfly loved windows and walls.

It banged into them.

The pebble told it:

You'll slam into the window again.

That wall is hard.

The lightbulb will burn you alive.

The fly now hated the pebble,

and wondered what it had liked about it in the first place.

It remembered: the pebble looked like a piece of chocolate cake.

The Synesthesia of The Infinite

We are all synesthetes. We replace things with words. Certainly as odd as colours for numbers.

NB

Yeah, I use synesthesia pretty loosely. But if a word was ever crying out for it…

Literacy

I'm not sure it means what we think it means.

John Gray and (the) Beyond

The dimensions we confer on the Unknown are our own – the same terrified human projections; what we bring to the mysteries of death, causation and the universe confirm our own limitations, and nothing more.

And what are we like? Pocked with pettiness, we love power plays; we luxuriate in supplications, and have a degenerate desperation for control. For these reasons I eschew ritual and religion. It's not that I think I'm superior; quite the contrary: I know my place. Besides, everything the world has ever said to me has been voiced with a beautiful clarity; truth doesn't hide behind bullshit and speak in riddles like we do.

Moron Mediums

I keep saying the medium is in danger, if not terminal. Information – what used to be its raw material – has supplanted it. Now, optimistically, I entertain the notion: maybe *ordering* is the next medium; we all do it differently; there's scope for a future. This must have been said already.

Scottish Independence

You and everyone else tell me how much you love me – of late. You've almost never been *genuinely* abusive and even I can see that when I've felt abused it's been jealousy of your standing (how much richer and more admired you are!) mixed with an overreaction to your consistently patronising attitude towards me. Hang on…

There's also your hideous personal history, that simply by association mars me. And, your utter lack of self-respect, which to you is nothing less than the motor of victory. Those with the lowest motives you exhort to clamber up and stand beside you.

In some ways – I can see – it's not just you. This is the world we live in.

I suppose the assumption is that without your money and the security your position provides I will be very much at risk, adrift. But why would that scare *you*? You're too canny to be motivated by sentiment. So…

I ask myself again, my self-esteem's that low: what do you gain from my deep oil, the shape I cut against the sea, my open, sewn-down arms?

The Strange Lass of Lawside

I met a woman who insisted she was celibate. She said she made an exception in the case of her husband, with whom she was very close. An odd distinction, I know. She and her husband live in an old manse, with a walled garden the size of a park, near the Law, in Dundee. She told me she never had visitors. I only met her when I worked for the census. These facts came to light in the course of the questions I asked. I ticked 'married', 'homeowner'.

Insides

When I was four I heard that someone got stabbed in front of Zabar's. I imagined the rip in the body neat as a zip. Inside I could see: a corn on the cob and a Milky Way in its wrapper. I wanted to go and get the food out.

More Upsides of Obscurity

You'll never have to listen to an actor read your writing on the radio.

Low Blow

If you want to know who slept with who: google image search. They're two rows down.

Nostalgia

Is it just me, or was there a lot more coloured toilet paper in the 70s?

Christmas Spirit

How many days of eating only After Eight mints 'til you die?

Friendship

Once you get to know them, everybody seems lonely.

How to Find What's Lost

Put what you seek out of your head and look everywhere and at everything. A genuinely more effective method; the key is in removing your goal. The sock or glasses turn up much faster. When you hold the missing object in your mind's eye, it serves only to distract, hamper and frustrate you. This also sometimes works on people, though admittedly with less success. To see them you must remove your own desires. In art – I wouldn't know; I've never managed it. I'm always burning with some shite to say.

Things my Dad Said About Love

My father told me that being in love was really the only thing to live for. He said love had a lifespan that – like the number of breaths for a yogi – can be extended or can contract, depending on the frequency of contact.

He also said that being a heroin addict was literally like having a monkey on your back: a huge and all-encompassing responsibility.

And finally, one other thing he told me was that one morning – after a final and terrible break-up with his girlfriend – he took the dog out onto 27th Street for a walk. He said the very air he breathed was full of hope and possibility, and that there was no greater relief than heartbreak.

Courtesan

I might have a cynical attitude towards love… or maybe you have a cynical attitude towards work.

Listen Carefully

Intense attention is the great unsung analgesic.

Nature Walk in Tenement Kitchen

Obsessing about something on my face, I lean near my reflection in the dark kitchen window and hear pigeons. Alighting, having sex, fighting? Who cares. It's the sound of their wings beating the air. It's the air.

If I'd sought *out* nature – told myself to pay attention, look for it – the weight that was lifted just then wouldn't have been. I'd have a far less precious sense: the observer had observed what she came to observe; or even ... she felt what she sought to feel. That's not that fun. Let it be done. Let it be done to you.

Why I Can't Look at Old Photos

They make me cry. I want to go back. It isn't that I was happier then – it's the moment being gone. The me in it. The you. The old road through the park. The demolished house. The gone shop. Are you like this? Do you want to go back? I want to see all the things I didn't see; I even want to see the things I did. I want the moment again and again and again. I'd never be bored. I guess that's my greed. If only it were for something possible. Then maybe I'd understand satisfaction.

Anyway, I have a friend who says we do and will. We will see our children as babies. See each other for the first time. If that's true, then that's ok.

Nihilists

The biggest hearts I know belong to people who are considered nihilists. It isn't that they believe in nothing. That's just what it looks like. Actually, what they love are things so tiny most people can't see them.

The Fountainhead and Freedom

Is it just me or are Richard Katz and Howard Roark similar? Maybe when Americans write fat novels of ideas there has to be a far-fetched embarrassment of a character who makes his ideals literal, while also making the ladies melt – before, during and after their ill-treatment. (He'll work with his hands, and be in the building trade too!)

What is the Novel of Ideas Anyway?

I guess *Freedom* really isn't. I mean, it's *called* 'Freedom', and we see the long point he's making – either about there being too much, or not enough, or both in different ways – but that doesn't make it, technically, a novel of ideas. According to the definition I just read online.

Randomer

I console myself with the coming death of standardised spelling and the birth of new words. The other day my daughter referred to someone as 'a randomer'. I thought that was a good word; comes in handy.

Christmas Past

A randomer had come into my room. He was sitting in my old lady chair by the window with his feet tucked up under him. He had his broad back to me. I was worried, but he explained that he owned the property.

I believed him; why shouldn't I? Besides, I had never met the owner – this might as well be him. He had come in the window, he said, and he planned to leave again the same way as soon as he explained to me about how to keep the tub from overflowing. I told him I never used the tub; what did I look like, someone who had time to take tubs?

He said he was just making sure; it must be the lad above. He said he could tell from my hands that I wasn't lying and that I worked a lot. I said, but how could that be? The water would come through my flat.

The landlord said, no, no *it* can. *It* can go down, through the walls, and come out at the bottom.

I didn't like the way he refused to use the word *water*.

Then he swung himself out of the chair and onto the fire escape in one movement. Outside he got caught on a net of Christmas lights I had put up. He had one leg on the ladder and he tried to unhook himself, muttering *these are a fire hazard*. Then he disappeared down, very quietly, like a cat.

Inside, I immediately went to look in the bathroom mirror. Everything was as it should be. The man across the courtyard was washing his feet at his sink and he scowled at me.

I put the kettle on, but couldn't help feeling like the landlord hadn't left yet. The static of the light bulb was noisy. The street made deep thuds. All the sounds seemed to take on his presence, and I kept seeing movements out of the corner of my eye.

Incarnation

You always thought you were fast-tracked from slug to human, some whim or coincidence; maybe you were boiled for the stew that saved the king's life. I've always had the sense I followed someone here – someone I met in a bar five minutes before, but was convinced I was madly in love with. I think I *knew* where we were headed. That's the worst of it.

Romantic Love

Why is it any shallower to love someone for who people think they are than for how they look?

Poor Barthes

How could he have known that for longstanding couples of a certain social echelon, the migration of *A Lover's Discourse* from library shelf to kitchen table is the worst sign in the world.

Too Much Proof?

Judging by the statistics, flying is safer than being alive.

That Old Photo on the Cover of This Book

Is my great-grandmother's grandmother. Doesn't the table she is leaning on look like her pelvis and legs? And the buttons on her dress that lead up to her brooch are like her spine which ends with her voice.

A Change in the Memes of Production

I could just get the word 'typo' tattooed on my arm. Put a heart around it.

I've said this before, and maybe it's just wishful thinking, but I believe within the next century standardised spelling will die.

Die! Die! Die! Your reign of terror *will* end. You fascist language eater! Killer of legitimacy! Box-ticker! Shallow ninny! Etc.

Dictionaries are about meaning, btw. And history. Not fucking spelling.

Ahem.

And you know what else? I *like* reading things that are spelled funny, having to pause and think: playfe, what the heck did that mean?

Printing press = standardised spelling.

Internet/autocorrect/texting = you get the idea.

Fonix

The name says it all; a piss-take. It's got to be the worst way to teach children to spell in our schizophrenic language. Thank god we're headed back to the days of having no orthography. What came with the printing press will go with it.

First Rule of Write Club

I once heard Kenneth Koch say something so stupid about T.S. Eliot it rendered me unable to read Eliot (at the time my favourite poet) for two years.

In 1991 a teenage girl in a creative writing class at SUNY Purchase said that the watermelon in *Lady with a Lapdog* ... I can't bring myself to repeat what she said, but it was twenty years before I opened Chekov again. How I love to talk to myself and myself alone about what writers meant.

Ruined Words

Words can go to the bad too. Remember when 'windows' meant windows? The word had an airy, Hart Crane-y feel. You see a poet eating a sandwich, looking out one, deciding his heart was too broken ...

And what about 'amazon'? The name has lost a fair bit; its connotation of wild nobility largely supplanted with this: £0.01 (plus shipping). Then there's 'value', which seems now to mean simply cheap. And that's to say nothing of that lost Queen of Insults, she who we could only aspire to be: 'bitch'. These days anyone can be anyone's.

Byron

I love the fact that Byron ate soy sauce. It makes me so happy. It makes my heart sing.

Paper Route

My dad used to pay me to find crumbs of cocaine on the floor. It was done in a sporting spirit, and I enjoyed it. It didn't seem strange to me and the truth is it still doesn't. Model airplanes? *That's* child abuse!

The Writer's Writer's Writer's Writer

If I was queen of the world and a great writer I would select those to whom I'd pass on my knowledge. They would have to take this test first: we'd read a whole novel and the only question I'd ask at the end was: which passage was its author's favourite?

Literary Androids

I'll just out and say it: I think they're among us.

The Deserving

Avoid them. They're cut-throats. Those who think they deserve love, acclaim, punishment, failure – are driven by the misperception that good works and hard work are rewarded, and skiving and bad deeds punished. Five minutes' reflection will prove this totally inaccurate. All we can do is pursue what we think is important, factoring ourselves as far out of the equation as possible, and see what happens. When you do this you find yourself in a pretty open field; much less limiting, far more varied and surprising.

When you do something for the sake of its outcome and then the outcome is not what you want, you get pissed off. You blame your friends, you blame a conspiracy of humans. Accept that life works in a far more mysterious way – or doesn't work at all, whatever you want to call it – but for god's sake stop groping around as if one day fate will dole out what you deserved. It might. It might not. Sometimes your aims appear to bring you close to what you want, sometimes they seem to push you away from it. In fact, the two are unrelated. That's it.

Blessed are the Cheesemakers

It strikes with the force of divine revelation: revenge needn't be all bad! What if the recipient is better off for it? What if they learn something valuable, something of benefit not just to themselves, but the world? The pleasure of watching them suffer is simply a bonus; and even if we err, and it is our motivating factor – it's ok, because all's well that ends well.

Sadly, that is where the trouble started. It's proven beyond doubt that humans can't be trusted with doling out punishment or reward. We have to leave it to chance. It may not be better for everyone; but it's better for you.

The New Town Crier

Oh Paper! Dear, dearest Paper! I love your physicality; you are all skin. I put my face under your arm; your smell enthralls me, always slightly different, depending on the weather and what you were thinking about. I love turning pages. The moment where I wait for you; then you arrive, right on time, and tell me everything. I even like your attendant metaphors. The best put-down of all time is one of yours: she couldn't ____ her way out of a paper bag. It works for everything: fuck, dance, punctuate. Also: papery and paper thin, rolling papers, yesterday's papers...

Some glossy pages curl. Paperbacks that jump into the bath bloat like corpses. Cheap old pages turn orange and brittle. I've seen black letters bleed like melanomas.

Now someone wants me to read on a Kindle. Christ, I just realised the sinister connotation of the brand name. Believe me, these fucks over at Amazon mean business! JB would certainly have been shoving a subliminal tit in your Coke advert, back in the day. No matter how much I hate the *The Armies of the Night* I'd never want to burn it.

The irony is that Steve Jobs was the last man with a sentimental finger on the baby boom pulse. We don't need to mimic nature or our bodies anymore. Technologies did grow out of what was to hand, but we are getting on in years, and the origins of our inventions are harder to see in our products. What do we lose? Only the deep and lovely grounding variations of our own physical experience of being here. If you don't know what I mean, you're lucky.

Bury me in a paper coffin with my cuddly iPhone 3.

Wealth

Have you ever noticed how people who say 'you make your own reality' are always really rich?

Not Again

If you're trying to free yourself of all desire then you probably have the desire to free yourself of all desire.

Holy Ghost

The moment between knowing what you need to write and trying to do it is sacred. Unfortunately, that moment is currently about six years long.

Facebook

Wasn't the high school cafeteria bad enough?

Life After

When I drink I am unpredictable, and that worries me. I might wake up happy or sad or full or tired. Sober I wake like a child; always myself, always waiting. But as a child I waited to be an adult, I wanted the narrative of my own making to begin; I would be an author of wonderful agency. That having turned out (as we know) to be far from the case, I wait now ... I suppose, for death. I don't want to hasten it. I do like it here. But I am curious. I have this bizarre conviction that everything will become clear when I die. Why on earth do I think that?

My Haunt

In some past lives I am already dead. I am a ghost who follows you. I watch you eat in restaurants, and lay with you in bed. Then when you die I find you; once you come back to life, I choose a body too. We are both here. Until I die. But I just become a ghost again, right by your side. I'll never come back to life before you. I'll never go away.

Neither a Real Paradox nor a Real Solution

Short-term and long-term solutions are often opposites. But it's not a real paradox; when it comes to human problems the word solution is impossibly optimistic. It should be reserved for liquids with stuff dissolved in them.

Gin on the Train, Blood on the Tracks

The most wonderful thing in the world is a gin and tonic before noon, poured out for you by a waiter, in a first class carriage. It makes me feel like Tom Ripley! Until it's finished ... see previous. Still – perhaps meaningfully – gin and tonic *is* a real solution.

Reading is Thinking

Sorry if I sometimes express myself less clearly than I might. It comes about naturally and then I leave it. I stick with the word that's hard to understand because I think tripping on it – on that little incision or rut – is useful. You get stuck, or maybe fall; and as you pause or pull yourself up, you look around.

Sad Truth #3572

Now that I don't drink I'm never sentimental. Some of my best writing sprang from grappling with that great, shit-coated dragon Cheap Sentiment; I'd wrestle him into submission with gracile aplomb, but *he* was still there, panting under me. Without all that nonsense, well, I don't feel like writing much.

Chemistry

Love corrodes.

Edinburgh

When you first come here it's easy to mistake its neutrality for indifference. But Edinburgh's balanced view is the hard-won detachment of lifetimes of effort. Generations of people have taken consciousness seriously here.

Lit Crit Fascist

Jane Eyre should only be sold in a double edition with *The Tenant of Wildfell Hall.* Anne was the smart one.

The Heart of an Artichoke

No, there is no reason why it should matter that you are only interested in what people think of you. It need not affect your relationships. Your work will still go over well, or it might not. When you're dead the same applies – there's no correlation. So don't worry – all that's determined by your inner life is your inner life.

Medusa

We love a brilliant man – St Augustine, Kierkegaard, Nietzsche – who has internalized his hurt, bitterness, and contempt, and thought his way to genius. The energy of anger and aggression turned inward produces a divine spectacle of lights, in the right hands. When a woman does it the world turns to stone. Just saying.

Lucky Painters!

Oh, for a bit of that reverential awe viewers lavish on inscrutable paintings. They seem to almost welcome having nae fucking idea what the art means or is about. But, God forbid a *reader* gets lost for a second; then the writer is considered incompetent. I think it's time to re-read the Preface to *Lyrical Ballads*; I have a feeling this trouble started around then. Before the dumbing down of literature we all read the Bible. Talk about stories that make no sense!

Nursery Rhyme

1. Ideally, the novelist uses all her strength to hurt her characters (it's very painful to hurt them), but is soft on herself (cue Edith Wharton's page fluttering from her bed, to be picked up by her maid).

2. If I hear one more word about the fucking Journey the top of my head is going to fall off and an army of cockroaches is going to march out singing the Cuban national anthem.

3. The more I look at it, the more worried I become about Narrative. A book about plays cites several plots, in all of them the woman is after one thing.

4. Time was I would fall in love with a different guy about every three years and have a baby about every four. Put that in your brain chemistry, hormone-stink shoebox diorama.

5. The Story and all its parts, its reliance on conflict as fuel – did it ever occur to you that that was a technology, an innovation – that before that life was conceived differently?

6. I use so many metaphors and double entendre because I enjoy using them – and I think a simple answer often doesn't meet the reader. A metaphor comes to you. I also enjoy chiasmus.

7. Don't think I haven't noticed that the way I think is similar to the way some people think about sex. A continual, nagging fixation. I met RD Laing once. He was an old man and my ex-boyfriend was buying his piano.

I do

This doesn't mean that marriage and long-term relationships are doomed; just that we should be a bit more honest about what happens. If we are more honest our relationships will survive, and we can fall in love as often as we do.

No. 9

I met an auld dear and her charcoal poodle in the park. She said, 'She's 14. She's blind and deaf. She's very good'.

I said, 'Mine is 5'.

9 years ago my daughter was 4. In 9 she will be 22 and I'll be 50. My dog will be 14 and may be deaf and blind.

And all that if we're lucky.

Light Reading

Always a mistake. I bring a slim volume of Sherlock Holmes on the train, hoping because this is a later novel it won't be racist. Duh. Page 28, '…being a huge and hideous mulatto, with yellowish features of a pronounced negroid type.' Stopped there.

Why can't they excise it? Here's what I think: teach 'Great(?) Racist Authors' (as we know the list is only slightly shorter than the one without the word racist in it) in every high school in America. Show kids exactly where the hatred is and investigate how it affects the author's worldview and work in general. Consider the very real possibility that racism disqualifies an author from greatness.

Next look at sexism.

And finally the narrative structure and how hate might be integral to it.

Thankfully, the LRB is skinny so I brought that too.

See Through Me

When I was little, other people's houses were possibilities. There was order, and you might be accepted by them if you were charming and flattered them, but were also earnest and smart and presentable and polite... But they don't take you in, ever. You can never be them. You have to offer yourself in exchange to be let in. And they always resent your desperation. I cried all the time. The boys said they were crocodile tears. I hated the implication that I could control it. I was like a shower. I cried and cried. Depending on the cause, tears tasted different – they were heavier or saltier, and the breathing changed. The worst was being misunderstood, misrepresented, misinterpreted or flat out lied about. That caused me to hyperventilate. As I got older, I realised (seemingly one by one – it took so long!) that I wouldn't want to be other people, or live in their houses. Because they couldn't know me. They didn't seem to try. I spoke to blank stares. This is how I ended up almost translucent. I want so much to be clear. I'm standing right here and you can see for yourself the wall behind me, or the tree, or whatever.

Tell Me a Little About Yourself

I like it when the writer lets me in and tells me what they are doing, or trying to do. Especially when they are smart, especially when they are unsure. Why is this seen as weakness? It's the opposite. And because Art is Great, self-consciousness can be made beautiful. Why are you afraid of questions? Then again, maybe it's just in the novel that self-consciousness is awkward. And we all know the novel is a lower artform. Literature's pop song. These days even TV shows are better.

Pop Culture

When do I get to stop feeling shitty about myself for not being a movie star?

The Other Thing Is

Try to remember that most people are doing the only thing they can. Myself included.

Little Respect, Less Power

Respect is one of those words that appears when concrete examples won't do; always a bad sign – a word whose power depends on being abstract. All meaning is concrete first. Anyway, back to the subject: shouldn't respect just be a constant? Shouldn't we impregnate all details with respect? Respect the tomato on your sandwich! Respect all dogs – even that poor Chihuahua with the over-active thyroid and permanently broken jaw! Respect everyone you don't know! (And never make the mistake of doing so by thinking they are like you.) (And for the naysayers out there, don't worry, there's plenty of time for people to lose your respect – so what's the hurry?) Back to the main point: regrettably the term respect is most often pulled from the thaumaturge's hat – it's a good trick and restores his power over the audience. But what he's after, what he calls respect, isn't. It's submission; it's suspension of your own self-respect, of what you know to be true. For this reason, any request for respect should be looked at very closely. If it requires that you sacrifice your self-respect – hit the road. Leave the theatre. Demand a refund. And no – self-respect isn't very abstract. I'm not sure why. Respect is a big limestone library. Self-respect is a hot dog cart outside it.

Pica

I saw a picture of a brain; a photo, not a drawing or fashionable CGI elaboration of circuits and sections. This was a big pink pile with a distinct (wider than I imagined) ravine. And I wanted to eat it.

(Also, looked up pica. Capitalised: genus of magpie. Lower case: what I'm talking about. From Latin for magpie. I love words.)

Wee Heresy in Her Filthy Pinny

The regalia of belief sparkles so. How pretty these cultures and arts, those sciences, hard and soft. The truth changes; what earth is, animals, oceans, sky, space, mountains, genders, species. Today we are neuro-assemblages. Today, purpose and self-advancement are one. (Sometimes you need to look a little closer to see this, sometimes you have to pull away.)

What is proven – what is true, in every human epoch – is like a dazzling crown, so finely wrought. The design draws us in, makes us want to know its every man-made angle; it makes us forget we'll never know what the fuck is underneath.

Solipsist

I am the dead.

Let's Call the Whole Thing Off

For you, boredom is the absence of stimuli. For me, it's often the presence.

My Corpus

For years I did things I couldn't stomach and my stomach hurt all the time.

Double Bluff

What I've learned is so so simple; it sounds naïve if I'm not careful.

Dear Friend

It's not that your husband is hiding who he is.

The Celebrated Scarlatti

Why do beautiful things make you cry?

Voice

Crossing the park, I hear a man's voice rise above the playground. He's behind the climbing frame. I thought maybe he was that guy who recites poetry off by heart, overblown things by Dylan Thomas. Maybe he's on the path behind, passing the park? But his voice is stout, not unearthly. No, the hidden father has a voice from years ago: deeper, more assured of Britain's place; melodious, a singer in his church choir. The sound of a bell tolling.

Thrift

When the day-to-day bullshit of your life has been supplanted by a 'communication technology' sugar-drip you no longer want to escape. Have we finally managed to erase life's empty minutes? We're gonna really regret it.

Sundial

Take this small phallus of time. It reminds me of math, the wrong kind.

Hypochondria

To what extent is it just a desire to be told our span, 'how long we have'? We waste years guessing.

Birthday Miracles

Fluoxetine, why do you don that wee green coat? Solpadeine Max, your fizz lifts morning like a long skirt over a puddle in the gutter. Even bland aspirin, made of the willow's bark, eats warts and scars, and loosens human hearts.

Serpent's Tail

I'll never understand what lyrical means.

Bye Bye Madame B

She has taught me a lot about death. Now she hangs around all corners of the kitchen ceiling simultaneously. Like dust. Like bats.

Entertain Me

Would a subversion of entertainment be boring? What is the opposite of entertainment? Are opposites subversions? Sometimes? My toast is ready.